Targeting Comprehension

Year 5

· Peter Alford and Aimee Bloom ·

PASCAL

Targeting Comprehension Year 5

Copyright © 2020 Blake Education
Reprinted 2021
ISBN 978 1 925490 64 0

Published by Pascal Press
PO Box 250
Glebe NSW 2037
contact@pascalpress.com.au

Authors: Peter Alford and Aimee Bloom
Publisher: Lynn Dickinson
Editor: Marie Theodore
Typesetter: Stacey Grainger
Series consultant: Del Merrick
Printed by Prinpia Co. Ltd

AUSTRALIAN CURRICULUM CORRELATIONS: English

YEAR FIVE

LITERACY

Interpreting, Analysing and Evaluating
Identify and explain characteristic text structures and language features used in imaginative, informative and persuasive texts to meet the purpose of the text (ACELY1701)
Navigate and read texts for specific purposes applying appropriate text processing strategies, for example predicting and confirming, monitoring meaning, skimming and scanning (ACELY1702)
Use comprehension strategies to analyse information, integrating and linking ideas from a variety of print and digital sources (ACELY1703)

LITERATURE

Examining Literature
Recognise that ideas in literary texts can be conveyed from different viewpoints, which can lead to different kinds of interpretations and responses (ACELT1610)
Understand, interpret and experiment with sound devices and imagery, including simile, metaphor and personification, in narratives, shape poetry, songs, anthems and odes (ACELT1611)

Contents

• HOW TO USE THIS BOOK •

A good understanding of comprehension is essential for effective writing and communication. This book gives you the skills to read between the lines. It contains activities for Literal and Inferential comprehension.

Literal comprehension is simply understanding exactly what the text says. Inferential comprehension is more complicated as it requires you to interpret ideas, intent or information in the text and to make assumptions. The activities in this book are intended to teach you how to unpick texts so that you can understand all the meanings embedded in them. In other words — how to read between the lines.

Inferential comprehension can be divided up into the following elements and each of them has their own sections in this book. They are explained using a variety of informative, imaginative and persuasive sample texts. The different elements are:

- **Literal** – understanding information and facts directly stated in the text
- **Inferring** – making assumptions based on context
- **Predicting** – imagining where aspects of a text may lead
- **Analysing** – interpreting the ideas behind what is written
- **Making connections** – finding links between two elements of a text
- **Critical reflection** – drawing on your own experience and knowledge to understand characters
- **Synthesis** – merging new information with existing knowledge to create new ideas

Also included is an assessment section for each of the seven comprehension elements and removable answers. Australian Curriculum correlations can be found on page ii.

TARGETING COMPREHENSION 5 © PASCAL PRESS ISBN 9781925490640

Quick Guide to:

• LITERAL COMPREHENSION •

Charlie ran towards the soccer ball as it sped across the field. "Come on! Come on!" he urged himself. Out of the corner of his eye, he spotted someone coming towards him.

Charlie drew his foot back, ready to kick the ball across the field when, suddenly, his ankle began to hurt. He fell hard onto the damp grass and clutched his newly bruised ankle. Staring up, Charlie squinted against the sun and saw Dylan sneering down at him. "Oops," Dylan said sarcastically.

Before he could utter a word, Sasha came running up. "Hey!" he called out. "I saw that — you tripped Charlie to get the ball."

"Maybe Charlie should just have run faster," Dylan smirked.

"I saw it too," declared Lisa. "You were being mean on purpose."

The two opposing teams gathered in around Charlie who was struggling to stand. "If that's how you want to play, you might need to find yourself another team," Lisa continued.

Dylan stood motionless, his mouth gaping slightly. No-one had ever stood up to him like that before. Left without a witty comeback, Dylan slunk off to the sidelines.

Answering questions about a text often means finding the answer in what you have read. Sometimes you are asked to look for, or remember, what was written in the text. These are **literal questions**.

> **Example of a literal question:**
> In the sample text above, the story is about a soccer player being unkind and hurting someone. Who was being unkind?
> **Answer:** Dylan. He was being mean on purpose.

DID YOU NOTICE?

The answer to a **literal question** can be found directly in the text. The answers are right there on the page.

Imaginative Text

Tyler kicked his skateboard to the kerb. He'd been trying to master a new skateboard trick all day and he was sick of falling off. Worse — he was just sick of failing.

Gemma saw Tyler slump on the bench next to the skate park and walked over. "Hey mate," Gemma smiled, "I noticed you're trying to nail an Ollie."

"This is dumb," Tyler scowled. "It's such a basic trick. I'll never get it."

"It took me a while too," admitted Gemma. "I didn't land one the first time, that's for sure. I'm not even sure I got it on the first day."

"Yeah, well, I just don't think I'm any good at this." Tyler looked at the ground.

"Not yet," Gemma shrugged, "but that doesn't mean you'll never be any good. You just have to keep trying."

Tyler sighed. "How about I give you a couple of tips?" Gemma suggested. "You never know, it might help."

"I guess it couldn't hurt," Tyler admitted.

"That's the spirit," Gemma grinned. "As my Uncle Tony would say: You have to believe in yourself."

1 What sport was Tyler learning to do? Tick the correct answer.
   a) snowboarding
   b) surfing
   c) skateboarding
   d) skiing

2 Where was Tyler skating? Tick the correct answer.
   a) his driveway
   b) the road
   c) the footpath
   d) a skatepark

TARGETING COMPREHENSION 5 © PASCAL PRESS ISBN 9781925490640

Imaginative Text

3 True or False? The trick Tyler was trying to learn was basic.

⬭ True ⬭ False

4 Colour the verbs (action words) mentioned in the story.

kicked   skated   shrugged

walked   carved   tumbled

bailed   scowled   looked

5 What advice did Gemma give Tyler? Tick two correct options.

a) You just have to keep trying.

b) Level out the board before you land.

c) You have to believe in yourself.

d) Make sure you always wear protective gear.

⬭
⬭
⬭
⬭

6 What did Gemma offer to do to help Tyler?

_____

_____

_____

Information Text

Did you know that 'matter' matters? Everything around us is made of **matter**. Matter is anything that occupies space and has mass.

Matter exists in different **states**: solid, liquid and gas. Liquids can flow easily, and we can pour them. Solids are things that we can pick up. However, we often cannot see or smell gases, for example the oxygen in the air that we breathe. Liquids, solids and gases are called 'states' of matter.

You can change the state of matter by changing its temperature. For example, if water is at room temperature, it's in a liquid state. If we place water in the freezer, it will become a solid known as ice. If we heat water hot enough it will turn into a gas, known as steam.

Understanding how matter can change states can be helpful. Whether you want to make a nice, cold ice block for a hot summer's day, or you'd like to melt some chocolate to make a yummy dessert, changing states of matter can be very tasty!

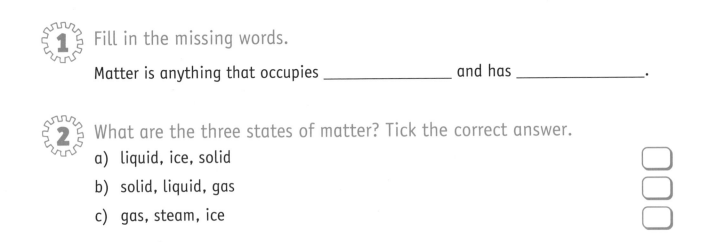

1 Fill in the missing words.

Matter is anything that occupies _____ and has _____.

2 What are the three states of matter? Tick the correct answer.

a) liquid, ice, solid ☐

b) solid, liquid, gas ☐

c) gas, steam, ice ☐

TARGETING COMPREHENSION 5 © PASCAL PRESS ISBN 9781925490640

3 Tick the best ending for this sentence. Liquids can be ...
a) poured easily.
b) picked up.
c) invisible.

4 Name an example of a solid from the text above.

_____

5 Name a gas we cannot see or smell.

_____

6 What can we change in order to make matter change states?

_____

7 Tick the best ending for this sentence. Water in its solid form is known as ...
a) water.
b) ice.
c) steam.
d) gas.

Persuasive Text

Plastic is Not Fantastic!

Have you ever wondered what happens to a plastic bag when you throw it in the bin? Or what happens to the plastic bottle you accidently drop on the ground? It's vital that we not only know the consequences of these actions, but that we also take steps to protect our planet.

Did you know that about 8 million pieces of plastic end up in the ocean every single day? Some people don't throw away their rubbish responsibly and these items end up in our waterways. This can be deadly for wildlife such as fish, dolphins and seabirds.

When plastic doesn't get recycled, it takes a long time to break down into the soil. A plastic bag can take up to 20 years to decompose and a plastic bottle takes 450 years! Throwing plastic in the bin sends it into landfill where rubbish is just buried in the ground. This process can leak pollutants into the soil and water.

So what should we do? How can we all help?

Firstly, everyone should make sure they recycle any plastic items that they use. Recycling plastic stops it from going into landfill. Recycled plastics can be made into lots of things, such as T-shirts, jackets, sweaters, carpets or even new bottles.

It's also important that we all minimise the amount of plastics that we buy. Using re-usable plastic bags and re-fillable drink bottles are two simple things that everyone should do. Making sure that we're not buying goods packed in unnecessary plastics, such as fruits and vegetables, is also something to be mindful of.

If we act now, we can protect our waterways and save our planet by planning ahead and being responsible for our use and disposal of plastics.

---

 1 How many pieces of plastic end up in the ocean every day? Tick the correct answer.

a) 8 billion

b) 8 million

c) 80

d) 450

TARGETING COMPREHENSION 5 © PASCAL PRESS ISBN 9781925490640

 Plastics in the ocean can be dangerous for which animals?

_____

 Match the item to the number of years it takes to break down in the soil.

Item	Number of years
plastic bag	450 years
plastic bottle	20 years

 Circle the nouns mentioned in the text that can be made from recycled plastic.

bags	jackets	sweaters
carpets	packaging	sleeping bags
shoes	bottles	blankets
T-shirts	toothbrushes	furniture

 Name two items we could re-use to reduce plastic waste.

_____

 What items are sometimes packed in unnecessary plastic?

_____

 Fill in the missing words.

Planning ahead and being responsible for our use of plastics can protect our

_____ and save our _____ .

Quick Guide to:

· INFERRING ·

Spiders, as a species, are very much maligned (rejected) and many people fear them. It's something about their creepy appearance, the way they scurry and the webs they leave. They are usually associated with scary, evil and sinister places in films. Because the first thing we see in many horror movies are spider webs, people link them with fear.

Spiders are actually quite helpful. Their webs helped win WWII. They were used to mark the view finders of bombers which helped the bombardiers locate their target.

Without spiders and their webs, other creepy creatures may dominate the earth.

Perhaps instead of slamming and damning spiders, we should all be singing *Fangs for the Memories*.

Answering questions about text often means finding the answer in what you have read. Sometimes you are asked to remember what was in the text. These are **literal** questions.

Example of a literal question:
The sample text above is about spiders and their webs. How have spiders been helpful to mankind?

Answer: During World War II spider webs were used in the view finders on aircraft to help guide the bomb to their target.

Unlike literal questions, when you **infer**, the answers are not in the text. You have to **guess the answer** by using information in the text. **Inferring** is guessing, using what you already know.

Example of an inferring question:
The writer infers that humans may be in trouble without spiders. What do you think the writer may mean?

Answer: Insects are caught in spider webs. I think the writer is inferring that the world may be threatened by insects if there were no spiders to catch them.

DID YOU NOTICE?

The answer to the question was not in the text. You had to look for clues to **infer (guess)** the answer by using the text. To do this, you needed to know that spiders' webs mainly trap insects. Knowing that all spiders are carnivores (meat eaters) may also have helped.

TARGETING COMPREHENSION 5 © PASCAL PRESS ISBN 9781925490640

Imaginative Text

Gran has told me a lot about the Eye. Now I wonder if she's been preparing me. I listen to her stories. I love my grandmother, but her stories sound so far-fetched, so unreal, I didn't believe them. My mother doesn't believe her either. We just listen to Gran's stories and dismiss them as just that — stories.

I have to see Gran because ...

But she is away visiting my Uncle Jack. She won't be back for three days.

Three days seems like a lifetime. I could ring her at Uncle Jack's. No — I don't want to talk to her about this over the phone.

Source: Laser Beams, *Eye of the Future*, Blake Education. [abridged]

 1 Why do you think Karen needs to talk to her grandmother? Tick the box of the best reason.

Karen wants to talk to her grandmother because ...

a) she believes that she too has the Eye.

b) she needs to ask how Gran's visit to Uncle Jack's went.

c) she wants to tell her grandmother that she has a new job.

d) she wants to tell her Gran that her mother doesn't believe her stories.

 2 In the text Karen says it 'seems like a lifetime'. Colour the arrow next to the best reason for this feeling.

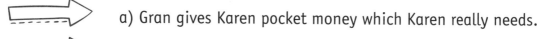 a) Gran gives Karen pocket money which Karen really needs.

b) Karen's mother is not interested in the Eye and Karen wants to talk to someone.

c) Karen wants to find out how her uncle is.

d) Karen is bursting to tell Gran that she thinks she has the Eye too.

Imaginative Text

3 What do you think Karen's grandmother has been preparing her for?

_____

_____

_____

4 Karen doesn't want to tell her grandmother on the phone. Shade the star of the statement that you think is most accurate.

a) Karen would rather not use the phone to talk about the Eye as it would take too long.	☆
b) Gran doesn't have a mobile phone.	☆
c) Karen has a lot of questions to ask about the Eye and wants to do this face to face.	☆
d) Gran doesn't like talking to Karen.	☆

Finally, it is Tuesday. My grandmother is due home today. I am stuck at school and the day drags. I have trouble concentrating. The second my last lesson finishes, I am out the door. I ride home at a speed that an Olympic cyclist would envy.

I dial Gran's number. My hand shakes with a mixture of excitement and nerves.

Source: Laser Beams, _Eye of the Future_, Blake Education. [abridged]

5 What is the writer wanting us to infer about Karen's feelings in class?

_____

_____

_____

6 Shade the speech bubble of what Karen plans to say on the phone.

a) "Hi Gran, I hope you enjoyed Uncle Jack's."

b) "Gran, I think I'm in trouble."

c) "Hi Gran, I need to come and talk with you."

TARGETING COMPREHENSION 5 © PASCAL PRESS ISBN 9781925490640

INFERRING

Information Text

> Built from 1949–1974, The Snowy Mountains Scheme was the largest engineering project ever undertaken in Australia.
>
> The Snowy Scheme was designed to collect water from the Snowy and the Eucumbene Rivers into dams and then use it to generate electricity. During the planning stages, it became obvious that there were not enough unemployed people in Australia to work on the project.
>
> The work was in harsh conditions, most of it underground. More than 120 workers died to build the Snowy Mountain Scheme.
>
> Source: Go Facts, *Migration*, Blake Education. [abridged]

1 How did the Australian government get around the problem of not having enough people to build the project? Tick the box of the statement that best explains this.

The government …

a) paid many people to leave their jobs and help build the project. ☐

b) offered free electricity to anyone willing to work on the Snowy Scheme. ☐

c) took people from the army to help create the Snowy Scheme. ☐

d) offered cheap travel to Australia for people willing to work on the Snowy Scheme. ☐

2 Why do you think so many men died during the building of the Snowy River Scheme? Tick any answers that apply.

a) There was a lack of clean air in the tunnels they dug. ☐

b) The men were homesick. ☐

c) There was the danger of rock falls and working with explosives. ☐

d) The men were old. ☐

Information Text

> World War II changed Australia's approach to immigration and the way it treated people born overseas.
>
> After the war the Australian government was keen to increase the population. It wanted to boost economic development and have more people to defend the country. British migrants were favoured. The government set up the Assisted Passage Scheme — British adults paid only £10 to move to Australia (their children travelled for free).
>
> Source: Go Facts, *Migration*, Blake Education. [abridged]

 3 Colour **two** main reasons why you think the government wanted more people to come to Australia.

a) It needed more workers on farms and in factories.

b) It wanted tourists to spend more money in Australia.

c) It needed to build a stronger army.

d) It wanted better food for its people.

e) Australia is a big country and they wanted people to fill it.

 4 It would have been difficult to encourage people to leave their countries and travel to Australia. Below are advertisements which may have been used to persuade people to travel here. Shade the most accurate ad.

Cheap travel to sunny Australia. What an offer! Fantastic cruise to a brilliant location.	Can't get better than this. Cheap travel to Australia. Everyone welcome.	Help build a new country. Jobs for all who take up our offer of cheap travel.

 5 Explain why you chose the advertisement you did.

_____

_____

_____

TARGETING COMPREHENSION 5 © PASCAL PRESS ISBN 9781925490640

ENDANGERED — THE HAIRY-NOSED WOMBAT

Once commonly found across a large part of Australia, the hairy-nosed wombat is now one of the rarest mammals in the world. If we aren't mindful of this particular species and its habitat, we will lose it forever.

The hairy-nosed wombat is a native Australian animal. It can grow up to 35 cm high, 1 m long and weigh up to 40 kg. Before Europeans came to Australia, this species could be found across Queensland, NSW and Victoria. By the 1900s, the hairy-nosed wombat could only be found in three small areas within these states. They are now only found in one area — Epping Forest National Park.

Wombats are burrowing animals — they dig tunnels underground to use as their shelter. This means they need soft, sandy soil in which to dig. A lot of the soil in Epping Forest National Park is made out of heavy clay, which means it's hard for them to find somewhere to dig their burrows.

Their diet consists of roots and coarse grass. However, a type of grass that was introduced from another country has now overrun Epping Forest National Park. Unfortunately, the wombats don't like to eat this grass, meaning that there is even less food than usual for them to consume.

Across Australia, we have destroyed our forests and bushland in order to clear land for farms and houses. Clearing land so that livestock have grazing land has forced wombats out of their natural habitat. The introduction of non-native grasses has also limited their food supply.

It's vital that we are more mindful of the impact that clearing land and introducing non-native plant species has on our animals. If we don't consider the consequences of our actions, we might lose even more than our beloved hairy-nosed wombats.

1 (a) Why might we lose the hairy-nosed wombat forever?

_____

_____

_____

(b) Why is this a problem?

_____

_____

_____

Persuasive Text

2 What is the author's point of view? Tick the correct answer.

a) We should be aware of how our actions affect animals.

b) We should relocate animals that are endangered.

c) We should breed more endangered animals.

d) We should not make any impact on animals' habitats.

3 The words below are from the text. Circle all the emotive words.

rarest	small	mindful	habitat
forever	consume	consequences	beloved

4 It is difficult for wombats to find suitable food to eat. Describe the impact this has on them.

_____

_____

5 If wombats become extinct, how could this affect the ecosystem?

_____

_____

6 How is this text connected to something you already know or have read?

_____

_____

7 Draw and label a flowchart or diagram depicting the impact of humans' actions on a different species.

TARGETING COMPREHENSION 5 © PASCAL PRESS ISBN 9781925490640

Quick Guide to:

• PREDICTING •

The old house on the hill was massive with seven gables, you know, the pointy parts of the roof. It was empty and creepy, maybe even haunted, but it was a place to explore and have a cracker of a time in.

For a hundred years, the house had stood on a hill overlooking our township, looking snobbishly down on the less fortunate. After its owner disappeared without explanation thirty years ago, most people in our town of three hundred steered clear of it. Spooky? Ghosts? No, none of that! The owner was a failed businessman who fled the country. For some reason the people he owed money to weren't able to sell the house to make up for their losses.

Once on the roof, it was simple to ease off some tiles and enter the cavernous roof space. Inside it was dark, dusty and laden with spider webs. Most kids would head the other way. Not so Teena and Tim. The twins really hadn't been introduced to fear. Skipping from one ceiling beam to the next, they avoided the almost paper-thin plaster of the ceiling and then that ...

Answering questions about text often means finding the answer in what you have read. Sometimes you are asked to remember what was in the text. These are **literal** questions.

Example of a literal question:
Why was the old house empty?

Answer: The house in the story was empty because the owner had left town.

Unlike literal questions, when you **predict**, the answer is not in the text. **Predicting** is guessing what may happen next in the text using what you have already read and understood.

Example of a predicting question:
What might happen next to Teena and Tim while they are in the roof?

Answer: Teena and Tim will probably fall through the paper-thin ceiling.

DID YOU NOTICE?

Predicting is a type of inferring requiring you to think about what **might happen** next. Inferring and predicting questions are like each other because the answers are not directly in the text. To answer these questions, you have to think about what you have read and use what you know to **guess the answer**. Predicting questions are about what you think will probably happen next.

Imaginative Text

> "That's it, I've had it! This is the *last straw!*" Kate threw her hands into the air in frustration and stomped down the hallway.

1 In what manner will Kate speak next? Tick your answer.

a) happily ☐

b) sadly ☐

c) calmly ☐

d) angrily ☐

> Kate's mum looked up from her desk as Kate stormed into the room. "What's wrong?"
>
> "Everything," Kate declared. "That little brat is ruining everything!"
>
> "Now, Kate," her mum began calmly, "that's not a very nice way to talk about your brother."
>
> "Well, ruining my life is not a very nice thing to do either," Kate fumed.
>
> Kate's mum took a deep breath. "Tell me what happened."

2 What do you think Kate's brother has done? Tick your answer.

a) something kind ☐

b) something funny ☐

c) something naughty ☐

d) something cute ☐

> Kate scowled, "This morning, he took a bite out of my apple while I was getting my lunch ready for school. He then drooled all over my homework book and now he's gone into my room and emptied my art supplies all over the floor!"
>
> "Hmm," Kate's mum said thoughtfully.

3 How do you think Kate's mum will react next? Tick your answer.

☐ calmly   ☐ angrily

> "Well, I can see why you're frustrated," Kate's mum began. "What did you do when he took a bite out of your apple?"
>
> "Well I had to get another one!" Kate exclaimed.
>
> "And what happened when your brother drooled on your homework book?"
>
> "I had to find a cloth and wipe it off!" Kate replied.
>
> "And why did your brother tip all your art supplies onto the floor?"

PREDICTING

TARGETING COMPREHENSION 5 © PASCAL PRESS ISBN 9781925490640

Imaginative Text

4 What reason will Kate give her mum? Tick your answer.

He tipped out my art supplies everywhere because he is ...

a) curious. ☐

b) creative. ☐

c) annoying. ☐

d) artistic. ☐

> "He tipped out my art supplies everywhere because he is a pain. He always ruins everything," Kate stated loudly.
>
> Kate's mum paused as she quietly walked up the hallway with Kate to her bedroom. "Did he ruin your lunch?" she asked.
>
> "Well ... I ... well, no — I got another apple. But —"
>
> Kate's mother gently took her hand. "And did he ruin your homework book?"
>
> "Well, I just wiped it off, but he shouldn't have —"
>
> Kate's mother wrapped an arm around her shoulder. "I know having a younger brother is sometimes hard. He's still learning the right thing to do, just as you were when you were his age." Kate's mum smiled as she looked into her eyes.

5 True or False? Kate will understand her mum's point of view.

☐ True   ☐ False

> "I know, Mum," Kate said sadly, "but just look at my room!"
>
> Kate's mum looked at the crayons, pencils and tubes of paint lying all over the floor.
>
> "Well, I guess we're all a little bit to blame," her mum said with a small smile.
>
> "What do you mean?" Kate asked.
>
> "Well, your brother did the wrong thing pulling out all of your art supplies. You did the wrong thing by leaving your door open when you know you should keep it closed, and I didn't keep a close enough eye on him this afternoon."

6 Do you think Kate will forgive her brother?

☐ Yes   ☐ No

> "I guess so," Kate sighed.
>
> "Come on, I'll help you clean up this mess," her mum offered, "and then we'll see what that little guy is up to."

Information Text

> The arrival of the British in Australia in 1788 changed the landscape of Australia.
>
> The colonists used British farming techniques. Some of these were successful, while others caused immense damage to the environment.
>
> The colonists needed to grow food to survive. They cleared native vegetation for grazing and crops. Since 1788, about 45 per cent of Australia's open forests and heath lands have been cleared.
>
> Source: Go Facts, *Reshaping Environments*, Blake Education. [abridged]

1 Farmers today would probably like to offer their advice to those early farmers. From what you have read, predict one important piece of advice they would give.

a) "Make sure you plan for enough water to be available." ☐

b) "Don't introduce foxes and rabbits. They eat too much." ☐

c) "Don't clear the land of all vegetation because it will become salty and water will wash the soil away." ☐

d) "Think about what you farm because it may not be profitable (make money)." ☐

2 Below are statements that tell of some of the effects colonist farmers had on the environment. Which one do you think is the most damaging effect?

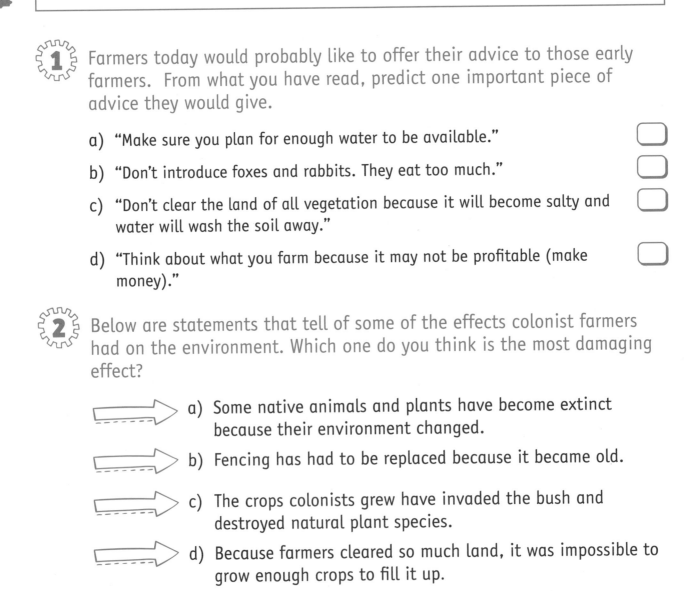

a) Some native animals and plants have become extinct because their environment changed.

b) Fencing has had to be replaced because it became old.

c) The crops colonists grew have invaded the bush and destroyed natural plant species.

d) Because farmers cleared so much land, it was impossible to grow enough crops to fill it up.

TARGETING COMPREHENSION 5 © PASCAL PRESS ISBN 9781925490640

One of the most destructive (damaging) animals introduced to Australia is the European rabbit. When the pastoralist, Thomas Austin, released 13 rabbits into the bush in 1859, he said they "could do little harm" and they reminded him of England. Within 60 years there were 10 billion rabbits in the country! A single pair of rabbits can produce 30–40 young every year.

Source: Go Facts, *Reshaping Environments*, Blake Education. [abridged]

 3 Rabbits destroyed natural plants, dug holes that lead to erosion and took over pasture land. Predict what the colonists did to fix this problem. Clue: Think about a rabbit predator.

_____

_____

_____

 4 Shade the circle below of the most accurate statement which predicts the 'rabbit industry'.

a) Rabbits were caught and used as pets by many people.	◯
b) Rabbits were used to help the environment by giving dingoes something to eat. This meant that fewer native animals died.	◯
c) Rabbit fur was used to make the felt of hats and some people used these animals as food.	◯
d) Rabbits dug large burrows which helped the wombats because they could use these instead of digging their own.	◯

 5 What do you think farmers are doing to fix some of the damage caused by poor farming practices? Colour your best prediction.

Farmers …

a) are fencing in their animals so they can't stray and eat the native plants.

b) are planting more native trees and trying to get rid of introduced pests.

c) are putting in dams to water native animals and trees.

d) have stopped sheep farming so that kangaroos can return.

Persuasive Text

PREDICTING

There is cause for alarm because BOY germs and GIRL germs **DO** actually exist!

Yes, all GOOD, sensible and responsible parents should take note of the latest research. Scientists studied the purple-bellied burbling rat and found male and female rats were healthier when kept apart. After a male rat escaped, he was found in the females' cage and became ill — so the answer was obvious.

When male rats were placed with females, the following symptoms occurred: silly smiles, heads full of clouds, crazed blabbering and weird 'cow-eye' looks. Principals are asked to take action, **NOW!!!!**

Anyone with common sense will see that these germs have awful results. Anyone uncaring enough to ignore this research may well be allowing harm to come to our children.

1 The writer of this article would like principals to take action. Predict the **first** thing you think principals would do if there was a real danger.

Principals would ...

a) inform parents of the danger via text message, email or letter. ☐

b) wait and see if the same symptoms occurred in their students. ☐

c) immediately send the children home and call a staff meeting. ☐

d) close all schools until the danger passed. ☐

2 Can you predict how other scientists may look at this research and point out its faults?

_____

_____

_____

_____

_____

TARGETING COMPREHENSION 5 © PASCAL PRESS ISBN 9781925490640

Persuasive Text

3 The writer used persuasive language and print to try to convince people that boy and girl germs are a worry. How was this done? Give examples.

_____

_____

_____

_____

_____

The Daily Blurb

Today, the government has decided to separate girls and boys in schools because of the danger of girl–boy germs being spread. Parents will now have to travel to the schools chosen by the Department of Education. Parents not …

Decision – Boys and girls cannot attend the same school.

4 This decision by the government would affect parents and kids. Predict the real problems that this decision could cause. Shade any that apply.

a)	Parents would not be able to sleep in each day.
b)	Families would have children at different schools.
c)	Parents would have to go to more meetings before school.
d)	Getting children to school on time would be far more difficult.

5 There is no such illness as girl–boy germs. However, if all schools did become only for girls or boys, what problems could this cause for schools, teachers and students?

_____

_____

_____

_____

Quick Guide to:

• ANALYSING •

Tides were huge in the northwest of Australia. That was something I noticed, but not quite as quickly as the searing heat.

In the south-west of our state the ocean rose or fell about a metre in 24 hours. Tidal movements up north came in at over ten metres. What did this mean? Going swimming meant heading off at high tide or on the rising tide. Beaches just disappeared at low tide.

'Newbies', people who had come to the north-west on holidays or as part of a journey, often didn't know that high tides could be dangerous. I noticed a man arrive in his beautiful new four-wheel drive vehicle with a sailboard on his roof racks. My family and I had come to the beach early and at low tide to collect oysters off the exposed rocks. Parking his car almost at the water's edge, the man unstrapped and assembled his sailboard and headed for the water. I ran up to him and started to tell him that he shouldn't leave his car there as the tide would soon come in.

He looked at me and said, "Go away kid, driven kilometres, buzz off!"

He left and, yes, the tide came in — pity about the car.

Answering questions about text often means finding the answer in what you have read. Sometimes you are asked to remember what was in the text. These are **literal** questions.

> **Example of a literal question:**
> Why were the family at the beach at low tide?
>
> **Answer:** The family had gone to the beach at low tide to collect oysters off the exposed rocks.

Unlike literal questions, when you **analyse**, the answer is not in the text. **Analysing** is reading and thinking about **all** the information, and deciding what the writer really means.

> **Example of an analysing question:**
> How did the stranger with the car treat the girl in the story? How would she have felt being spoken to in that way?
>
> **Answer:** The man treated the girl rudely and with arrogance. I think she may have felt a little hurt.

DID YOU NOTICE?

When you **analyse** text, you have to read carefully and use the information to make up your mind about **what is really meant**. When you were inferring and predicting you also had to do this. Analysing requires you to think about the whole text.

TARGETING COMPREHENSION 5 © PASCAL PRESS ISBN 9781925490640

Joel is ten years older than I am and works as a spray painter in a smash repair shop. I often call in after school to look at the smashed cars.

When I leave school I'm going to buy a Ford and be just like Joel.

Dad walked out on us when I was a baby. I don't know why. Mum thinks he's probably living in another state, nobody knows for sure because we never hear from him. It doesn't matter though because I've always had Joel to look out for me.

The girls in my class think Joel is good looking. "He's so cute!" they say whenever they see him. "Just like Brad Pitt."

At school, Mr Sams had some news for the class. He'd been offered a contract to go to England to play football for one of their big clubs.

Source: Laser Beams, *Teacher's Pet*, Blake Education. [abridged]

ANALYSING

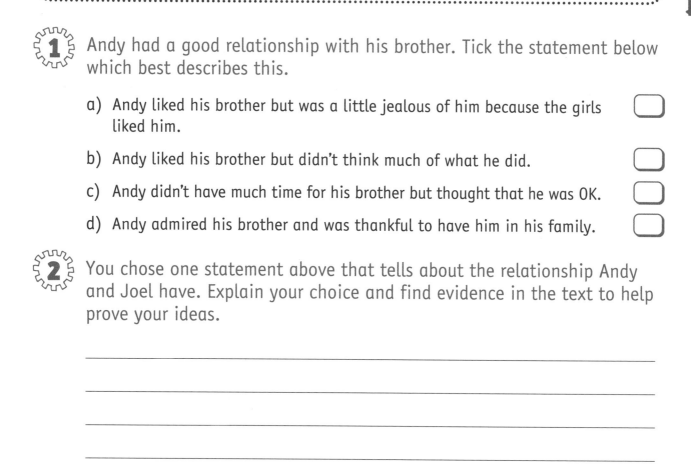

1 Andy had a good relationship with his brother. Tick the statement below which best describes this.

a) Andy liked his brother but was a little jealous of him because the girls liked him. ☐

b) Andy liked his brother but didn't think much of what he did. ☐

c) Andy didn't have much time for his brother but thought that he was OK. ☐

d) Andy admired his brother and was thankful to have him in his family. ☐

2 You chose one statement above that tells about the relationship Andy and Joel have. Explain your choice and find evidence in the text to help prove your ideas.

_____

_____

_____

_____

_____

_____

 3 Andy's father was not in his life. Shade the heart of the statement that best explains the way Andy felt about this.

a) Andy was a little sad and disappointed, but he had his brother and mum to care for him.	♡
b) Andy was OK with not knowing his father but would have liked to have known him.	♡
c) Andy didn't really care at all about his father not being around.	♡
d) Andy really disliked the fact that his father had walked out and didn't care.	♡

ANALYSING

Now, of course, his head was twice as big. 'Look at me! I'm going to be a big deal footy player in England.' He's leaving at the end of the week.

"You'll be getting a new teacher," he said. He thought we'd be sorry to see him go.

I wondered who the new teacher would be. "Couldn't be …"

Source: Laser Beams, *Teacher's Pet*, Blake Education. [abridged]

 4 Tick the best ending to Andy's sentence in the text. Think about Andy's relationship with Mr Sams.

Couldn't be …

a) as good as Mr Sams as a footballer.

b) worse than Mr Sams.

c) another teacher like Mr Sams.

d) another man teacher, I hope.

5 Write how you think Andy feels about his teacher, Mr Sams.

_____

_____

_____

_____

TARGETING COMPREHENSION 5 © PASCAL PRESS ISBN 9781925490640

Information Text

ANALYSING

Gold was discovered in Australia in 1851, triggering a mass influx (migration) of people seeking their fortune. Most gold-seekers came from Great Britain, but almost 40 000 people came from China. Only a small minority of Chinese were able to pay for their own voyage and come to Australia free of debt. Their wives and families remained in China.

The British colonists resented (didn't like) the Chinese even before gold was discovered. They treated the Chinese miners poorly. They didn't like their strange clothes, language and religion — and their competition for gold.

It was not just the Chinese the British feared. Asia was a mysterious and unknown region. Australia was large, under-populated and rich in resources.

Source: Go Facts, *Australia and Asia*, Blake Education. [abridged]

 1 How would the Chinese people have felt coming to Australia which was a strange land to them? Select the statement that you think is most accurate.

When the Chinese people travelled to Australia they …

a) thought it would be a fantastic holiday. ☐

b) thought that what they were doing was hard, but worth trying so they could have a better life. ☐

c) had decided that they wanted to find a different culture because they were discontented with their own. ☐

d) thought that it would be good to help build a new nation. ☐

2 Why would it have been hard for the Chinese people to come to Australia — apart from the different culture, climate, food and way of life?

_____

_____

_____

_____

_____

Information Text

 3 The following headlines are from newspapers in the 1850's. Shade the one that has come to be true and is now accurate.

> Australia – a Fair Land for All

> Invasion from Asia Is Happening

> Our Gold and Resources Stolen by Others

> Australia Doesn't Deal with Asia

 4 Explain your choice of the headlines above.

_____

_____

_____

_____

_____

Did you know that the first Chinese-born settler in Australia, a carpenter named Ahuto, arrived in 1803?

Source: Go Facts, *World Events*, Blake Education. [abridged]

 5 Some Australians still worry about people coming here from other countries. They fear that migrants will not fit in because they have different cultures, beliefs and thinking to ours. Shade the shape that tells how migration has worked for our country up until now.

> Migration has worked because we have benefited from the different foods, skills and knowledge brought by migrants.

> Migration has really worked because we have lots of different fast foods.

> Migration has not worked because we still have a land that doesn't have many people.

ANALYSING

Driving to School is Not Cool

In the past, most kids walked to school or rode their bikes, but now almost everyone is driven to school. It's obvious that this causes a number of problems, including poor health, damage to the environment and even a lack of confidence.

Kids need to get enough exercise every day in order to be healthy. Being driven to school, instead of walking, is one reason why kids aren't getting the exercise they need. By walking to school every day, kids will become more active and grow healthier, stronger bodies.

With so many kids being driven to and from school every day, there are more cars on the road than ever before. This creates more air pollution which is terrible for the environment. By walking to school, there will be fewer cars on the road and less pollution in the air, which is clearly better for the planet.

I believe some kids aren't confident to walk to school. It might be because they are very young or a bit worried about being without their parents. Sometimes, the parents are the ones concerned about their kid walking alone. One way to solve this problem is to organise a 'walking bus' and walk to school with other kids from your neighbourhood. Big kids can look out for little kids and help them feel safe.

Together, we can solve these problems. The solution lies in our hands and it's time to take action. We must begin to walk to school and encourage others to do the same.

ANALYSING

 1 Circle some of the emotive words that were used in this text.

must	obvious	damage
healthy	planet	action
terrible	organise	kids

Persuasive Text

2 Label the following sentences as Fact or Opinion.

a) Everybody should walk to school. _____

b) We need to exercise every day in order to be healthy. _____

c) Cars cause air pollution. _____

d) Some kids aren't confident walking to school. _____

3 Complete the table below using information from the text.

Problem	Caused by	Solved by
Kids aren't getting enough exercise.	a)	b)
c)	too many cars driving kids to school	d)
e)	f)	organising a 'walking bus' to walk to school together

4 Write another suitable title for this text.

_____

TARGETING COMPREHENSION 5 © PASCAL PRESS ISBN 9781925490640

Quick Guide to:

· MAKING CONNECTIONS ·

Snar Twerp had been dragged up, not brought up. His parents were never going to be nominated as parents of the year. If he didn't bring something of value home, he didn't eat, very simple really. Life as an eleven-year-old was a bit tougher for him than others of his age.

Flip Snodgrass was just the opposite. His parents were wealthy and he wanted for nothing. A click of the fingers and whatever he desired was delivered, same day and with a smile. Strangely, although Flip had every reason to be a spoilt brat, he wasn't. In fact, he had a strong sense of social justice. Flip knew that he was lucky, but for some reason, he looked out for people who were not born into money.

Standing behind Snar in a shop, waiting to be served, he saw that every time the sales assistant turned away, another item disappeared into Snar's pockets. Moving forward to be served, Snar held out a dollar for the small sweet he held.

Flip stepped in front suddenly and said, "My friend has stored a few things in his pockets that we need to pay for. What were they again mate?"

Answering questions about text often means finding the answer in what you have read. Sometimes you are asked to remember what was in the text. These are **literal** questions.

Example of a literal question:
Why was Snar stealing from the shop?

Answer: Snar had to take something of value home. If he didn't, he wouldn't eat.

Making connections starts with reading and thinking about all the text. These questions ask you to think about why things in the text are linked or have an effect on another piece of text or characters in a story. **Making connections** asks you to think how two or more different things or actions affect each other.

Example of a making connections question:
What were the differences in the way Snar and Flip saw the world?

Answer: Snar was looking at the world as being a desperate place. He saw life as a struggle. Flip saw that he had so much and thought that he should care for others who had less.

DID YOU NOTICE?

Making connections means thinking about two things in the story and working out **how these are linked or connected**. This may involve comparing and contrasting. This is the case in the example. The lives of the two characters were compared and the differences written about.

Kel flew around the track in her best time for the morning. It had only taken a few laps for her to learn the turns and twists of Ridgemont's track.

It hadn't been her choice to _____, but then, it never was. If Mum's work moved interstate, they …

Kel had got lucky this time to be close to her biggest love.

This track was laid out differently from what she was used to, but its flowing lines and interesting design made it fast and fun.

Everyone here seemed so friendly and welcoming, which made settling in a whole lot easier. Kel heard a loud voice coming from behind the drinks machine.

"Who's the new kid? Thinks he's pretty hot, doesn't he?" said the voice.

Source: Laser Beams, *Karting Kel*, Blake Education. [abridged]

MAKING CONNECTIONS

1 What had happened recently in Kel's life? Tick any statements that apply.

a) Kel was new to the sport of karting and was doing it for the first time. ☐

b) Kel was trying out a new track which had been built where she lived. ☐

c) Kel was new to the neighbourhood. ☐

d) Kel's parents had moved and she was starting at a new karting club. ☐

2 Explain why you chose the statements above. Use some of the text to help you explain.

_____

_____

_____

_____

_____

_____

_____

Targeting Comprehension
Year 5 Answers

· Literal ·

Page 2
1 c
2 d
3 True
4 kicked, shrugged, walked, scowled, looked
5 a, c
6 *Sample answer* Gemma offered to give Tyler some tips.

Page 4
1 space, mass
2 b
3 a
4 ice/chocolate
5 oxygen
6 temperature
7 b

Page 6
1 b
2 fish, dolphins and seabirds
3 plastic bag – 20 years; plastic bottle – 450 years
4 T-shirts, jackets, sweaters, carpets, bottles
5 re-usable plastic bags and re-fillable drink bottles
6 fruits and vegetables
7 waterways, planet

· Inferring ·

Page 9
1 a
2 d
3 *Sample answer* Karen's grandmother has been preparing her to use the Eye wisely.
4 c
5 *Sample answer* Karen is feeling very excited about the Eye and is looking forward to talking to Gran about it.

Page 11
1 d
2 a, c
3 c
4 Help build a new country. Jobs for all who take up our offer of cheap travel.
5 *Sample answer* This advertisement gives better information.

Page 13
1 a) *Sample answer* They might become extinct.
   b) *Sample answer* We won't have any more of this animal./We will be responsible for killing an entire species.
2 a
3 rarest, forever, mindful, consequences, beloved
4 *Sample answer* Without a reliable and suitable food source, wombats will die because they don't have enough to eat, meaning the population will shrink and wombats might become extinct.
5 *Sample answer* Other animals in the food chain could be impacted.
6 answers will vary: Students might mention other endangered or extinct species they are aware of.
7 answers will vary

Predicting

Page 16

1 d
2 c
3 calmly
4 c
5 True
6 Yes

Page 18

1 c
2 a
3 *Sample answer* The colonists trapped the rabbits and released foxes because foxes eat rabbits.
4 c
5 b

Page 20

1 a
2 *Sample answer* Other scientists might find fault with rats being used and not humans, and the attempt to interpret rat emotions.
3 *Sample answer* The writer used capital letters and bold print for some words, such as DON'T; underline for DO; exclamation marks; emotive language such as sensible, crazed, uncaring; fear of damaging children, such as 'harm will come to our children'.
4 b, d
5 *Sample answer* Parents would have to drop children off at different times and places; siblings would be split up; more travel time for some children.

Analysing

Page 23

1 d
2 *Sample answer* Andy admires Joel and he says he wants to be just like him; Joel looks out for him.
3 a
4 b
5 *Sample answer* Andy doesn't really like Mr Sams and isn't sad to see him go.

Page 25

1 b
2 *Sample answer* It would have been hard for them to leave their family behind, and people in Australia treated them differently.
3 Australia – A Fair Land for All
4 *Sample answer* Australia is a multi-cultural country and we have laws to protect us all from discrimination.
5 Migration has worked because we have benefited from the different foods, skills and knowledge brought by migrants.

Making Connections

Page 30

1 c, d
2 Everyone was welcoming which made settling in a lot easier.
3 a
4 *Sample answer* Marc probably thought girls shouldn't be good at karting.
5 c

Page 32

1 a/c
2 *Sample answer* Mrs Lee would have upset men in general, husbands and police.
3 Mary helped women take a big step towards equal rights for men and women.
4 We are so thankful for her work. – the poor
Women should be able to vote. – Mary
I do hope she is able to make this change. – many women
How dare she try to change things. – men at this time
5 *Sample answer* Women got the right to vote in other Australian colonies after South Australia.

Page 34

1 a
2 answers will vary
3 a – 1, b – 1, c – 2, d – 1, e – 2
4 *Sample answer* There would be increasing health costs, illness, and greater use of hospitals and doctors.
5 Kids need to get outside at times because their health may depend on it.

TARGETING COMPREHENSION 5 © PASCAL PRESS ISBN 9781925490640

6 *Sample answer* Too much screen time is dangerous. Kids may drop dead if they have too much. This statement threatens an extreme outcome – death.

• Critical Reflection •

Page 37

1 a – No
2 a) *Sample answer* The dog couldn't open the packets of food and there were tomato sauce handprints on the floor.
   b) *Sample answer* Parker didn't want to get into trouble.
3 frustrated, angry, tired, annoyed
4 a
5 a – No
   b) *Sample answer* The dog couldn't get the tissues out of the box and Parker had already made a mess in the kitchen.
6 b
7 *Sample answer* Parker will probably make another mess./Parker will get into more mischief.

Page 39

1 b
2 *Sample answer* 200 years ago, there were no phones, radios, computers and email. Even sending letters took a long time because they had to be sent by ship.
3 a, e
4 *Sample answer* When there are disasters now, help comes faster, aid is quicker, and more people and countries are involved.
5 People don't do well on their own. They need to communicate their thoughts and feelings to others.

• Synthesis •

Page 46

1 a
2 *Sample answer* Women are important in UN peacekeeping missions as they help reduce conflict, provide support and security for local women and children, and they also help to protect the rights of local women.
3 The colour of peace. – white
   The colour of nature. – green
   The colour of love and romance. – pink
   The colour of evil. – black
4 *Sample answer*
   White – colour of doves, peace, purity, surrender
   Green – colour of trees, plants, crops
   Pink – feminine, used for Valentine's Day
   Black – dark, sinister, night, fear
5 *Sample answer* Other countries probably think Australia's contribution is good and they feel grateful for our help.

Page 48

1 c
2 *Sample answer* Tourists would be afraid of Australian beaches and swimming. They may see Australia as a dangerous place and not come here.
3 *Sample answer* Get out of the water. Never dive alone.
4 *Sample answer* Taken by Shark!/Lucky Escape
5 *Sample answer* Cone shells may be dangerous because the toxin would prevent divers from breathing.
6 d *Sample answer* This proverb talks about jumping into the water without thinking and preparation.

ANSWERS

· Assessment ·

Page 50

1 True
2 Physical adaptations: Bodily features that help animals survive
3 d
4 False
5 behavioural
6 Labels should include: eyelashes, nostrils, hooves and hump
7 *Sample answer* It is important because camels can survive for many days in the desert without drinking water.
8 *Sample answer* Animal adaptations help them to survive.

Page 52

1 *Sample answer* a – 2; b – She hit her hand and hasn't created a successful invention yet.
2 c
3 *Sample answer* a – No; b – Her other inventions have failed and the electrical circuit didn't work.
4 b
5 True
6 d
7 *Sample answers* Something was wrong with the electrical circuit./Phillipa had soldered the wrong wires together./The electrical circuit didn't work.
8 Very unlikely

Page 54

1 b
2 Very quickly
3 Very likely
4 *Sample answer* a – No; b – The other driver is driving aggressively and might spin out or crash into the barrier.
5 c
6 c
7 False

Page 56

1 a, d
2 a
3 *Sample answers* To learn special skills to help their owners./To learn how to keep their owners safe.
4 *Sample answer* Guide dogs can help people who are blind or visually impaired to be safe, independent and more confident.
5 *Sample answers* The dog might not listen to the owner./The owner might not be safe because the dog is not paying attention.
6 b

Page 58

1 answers will vary
2 It will help kids become healthier and more creative./It will help develop active minds and bodies.
3 *Sample answers* ...feel frustrated because I don't have enough time to play/puzzled because I don't have to do any activities.
4 answers will vary
5 answers will vary
6 answers will vary

Page 60

1 *Sample answers* Dogs make good friends./Dogs make better friends than people.
2 b
3 a
4 b
5 Very true
6 *Sample answers* Dogs can't talk to you./Dogs don't really understand you./Dogs can't go everywhere with you.

Page 62

1 a – answers will vary; b – answers will vary
2 *Sample answer* Earth has the right conditions for us to live, e.g. temperature, water, plants and food.
3 c
4 answers will vary
5 *Sample answers* The Earth Is Special/The Earth is Unique/There's Only One Earth

TARGETING COMPREHENSION 5 © PASCAL PRESS ISBN 9781925490640

Imaginative Text

"If you ask me, you'd better watch out," answered Steve, the mechanic. "You might have some serious competition there."

Kel heard a snort in reply. Kel walked across to the drinks machine. Pushing in some coins, she selected her drink and then sauntered behind the machine.

Steve turned around. When he saw Kel, he gave her a grin. "Speaking of competition, here it is now, Marc. Meet Kel, the new kid in town."

Marc looked at Kel suspiciously as she removed her helmet.

The boy's face almost crumbled onto the concrete below. He stammered, "B … but … but you're a …"

Source: Laser Beams, *Karting Kel*, Blake Education. [abridged]

3 Marc was shocked to see Kel. Which statement is the best reason for Mark's shock? Colour the kart wheel.

a) Marc was shocked because Kel was a girl and he had expected that she would be a boy.	◯
b) Kel was a lot younger than Marc had expected. He thought she would be experienced.	◯
c) Marc was shocked by Kel because she had a weird haircut.	◯
d) Marc was upset with Steve because he thought that Kel may have been someone important.	◯

4 A **stereotype** is when people have an idea of something in their mind which is what they have come to expect. What stereotype do you think Marc may have had in mind?

_____

_____

_____

5 How did Marc see himself as a kart driver? Shade the shape below which you feel is most accurate.

a) "I like a bit of competition because I'm sick of winning."	▽
b) "As I am the best kart driver I don't need competition."	◇
c) "I'm the best kart driver here. There really is no-one who can beat me."	⬡

MAKING CONNECTIONS

Information Text

Mary Lee was a tireless worker for poor women and children in the colony of South Australia.

Mary was born in Ireland. She married and had seven children. In 1897, when Mary was 58 years and widowed, she immigrated to Adelaide to care for her sick son. Sadly, he died, but Mary remained in Adelaide. She began to work with poor families. She wanted to improve their lives and she believed the best way to do that was to give women the right to vote (suffrage). She saw this as her "crowning task".

Not everyone approved of Mary's ideas. At this time, few women spoke about their beliefs in public. Both men and women insulted and threw things at her. Eventually she achieved ...

Source: Go Facts, *Great Australians*, Blake Education. [abridged]

1 The following headlines may have appeared in a South Australian newspaper about what Mary had achieved. Tick the most likely headline.

a) Mrs Lee is a Troublemaker ☐

b) Mrs Lee Helps Poor Women and Children ☐

c) Mrs Lee Wins the Right for Women to Vote ☐

d) Mrs Lee Loses Her Son ☐

2 Apart from some women, who would Mrs Lee have upset so much that they abused her and why?

_____

_____

_____

_____

_____

_____

MAKING CONNECTIONS

TARGETING COMPREHENSION 5 © PASCAL PRESS ISBN 9781925490640

Information Text

3 Tick the shape that best tells what Mary achieved in Adelaide and Australia.

Mary helped women take a big step towards equal rights for men and women.

Mary brought better lives to those people who were poor.

Mary helped hospitals because her son had died of an illness.

Mary was really brave to have immigrated to Australia.

4 Draw a line to connect the thought to the right person.

Thought

We are so thankful for her work.

Women should be able to vote.

I do hope she is able to make this change.

How dare she try to change things.

Person

men at this time

many women

Mary

the poor

South Australia became the first colony in Australia to give women the vote. It was also the first place in the world to allow women to stand for parliament.

Men got the right to vote in South Australia in 1856, 38 years before women.

Source: Go Facts, *Great Australians*, Blake Education. [abridged]

5 What do you think may have happened in the other Australian colonies after Mary won the right to vote in her colony?

_____

_____

_____

_____

_____

MAKING CONNECTIONS

Persuasive Text

Text 1. Kids should have as much screen time as they want. Learning happens every time they sit in front of a device. Science says that you can lose weight and get muscle tone just by using your mind. Talking with others and being able to learn how to work with others are skills you'll never ever need. Only eggheads get anything out of exercise or making friends. Sitting on your bottom for hours a day does wonders for your health and mind.

Electronic games rule! Parents should get a life!

Text 2. Most parents agree that kids need a balance between sitting in front of a screen and getting exercise. Doctors are worried about kids becoming fatter and this will cost our country in the future. Australia can't really afford what will happen if we are all too large and unhealthy.

Devices have their place, but so does health. Health is really important and most people see this belief as being true. Really, people who care most about their children must limit their screen time.

MAKING CONNECTIONS

 1 These texts totally disagree with each other. Tick the statement that best explains these differences.

These texts disagree because ...

a) one says that too much screen time doesn't matter and the other talks about health and exercise. ⬜

b) one is right and the other is wrong. ⬜

c) the first text warns what may happen in the future and the other one talks about now. ⬜

d) the first text talks about what parents want and the second is about what kids want. ⬜

 2 Where do you stand on this issue? Think about what you've read and seen, and write a few sentences giving your opinion on this topic. **What do you think?**

_____

_____

_____

_____

TARGETING COMPREHENSION 5 © PASCAL PRESS ISBN 9781925490640

Persuasive Text

 3 The writers of these statements have been persuaded to take a point of view. Circle which text influenced them: Text 1 or Text 2.

Statements	Texts	
a) Well, if people know that screen time is good for you, why not do more?	1	2
b) When you get older and go to work, you don't have to know how to be with other people.	1	2
c) You may become ill if you spend too much time in front of a device.	1	2
d) Be sensible, you don't need to get outside to play games.	1	2
e) Sharon, get out and run around for a while.	1	2

4 What is the writer thinking may happen if too many people become overweight? What would this mean for our country?

_____

_____

_____

5 Tick the shape which most parents would think is right after reading both texts.

Too much screen time is dangerous. Kids may drop dead if they have too much.

Kids need to get outside at times because their health may depend on it.

Keep the kids happily sitting at a device. It isn't that bad for them.

6 One of the persuasive ideas in the previous question is 'over the top' (extreme). Write it down and say why you think it is extreme.

_____

_____

_____

_____

MAKING CONNECTIONS

Quick Guide to:

• CRITICAL REFLECTION •

Soft drinks like Cola are the nectar of the gods! Research has finally come up with extremely accurate information regarding these liquid pleasures. Some pretty basic knowledge really, that teenagers have known for years.

Sugar in soft drinks is actually good for us. Pimples, obesity (fatness) and terrible teeth are not really caused by drinking litres of the fizzy wonder fluids. Energy, clean-belching and a clear head are actually the side effects of these delicious brews.

Clean-belching may need some explanation to adults. When one clean-belches, because of soft drink, the body is ridding itself of noxious (poisonous) gas. If these vapours aren't expelled, they may slip out of somewhere else and nobody wants that! Phew! Pooh, definitely not!

Tired, with lack of energy? Doctors now recommend a litre of the 'good stuff' a day. At least that's what our company doctor and researcher Regina Toothrotinous recommends. Energy drinks are even better for those imbibing (drinking) because they ...

Answering questions about text often means finding the answer in what you have read. Sometimes you are asked to remember what was in the text. These are **literal** questions.

> **Example of a literal question:**
> What did researchers find about soft drink according to the article?
>
> **Answer:** The article states that soft drink is good for us because it helps with a clear head, clean-belching and energy.

Critical reflection starts with reading and thinking about all the text. These questions ask you to think about how things happen, how they affect what is happening and the feelings of characters.

> **Example of a critical reflection question:**
> The above article is biased as it only concentrates on one side of the argument. Are the facts in the text from a reliable source?
>
> **Answer:** No, the facts in the text seem to come from a company which appears to make and sell soft drink.

DID YOU NOTICE?

The answer is not in the text. You have to **read and decide** how the characters are thinking. You have to read and think about your feelings about a character, or about a topic. You have to **use your ideas** to find the answer by thinking of your experiences.

TARGETING COMPREHENSION 5 © PASCAL PRESS ISBN 9781925490640

Parker's mum walked into the kitchen with her empty breakfast plate. "Oh, Parker!" she exclaimed. "Just look at that mess!"

Cereal had been spilled all over the floor, alongside an open packet of biscuits with half the biscuits missing, and tomato sauce handprints lined the cupboard walls.

"What have you done?" Parker's mum shook her head.

"Wasn't me." Parker wiggled his nappy-covered bottom on the floor. "Dog," he insisted.

"It was the dog?" Parker's mum raised an eyebrow.

"Yes, dog." Parker wiped crumbs away from the corners of his mouth with sauce-stained hands and ran out of the kitchen.

Parker's mum sighed and began picking up the biscuits.

After some time, Parker's mum finally wiped one last crumb off the floor in the kitchen. "Parker?" she called. He had been far too quiet for far too long. Placing the cloth on the bench, Parker's mum began to walk down the hallway. "Where are you?"

A giggle from the bathroom gave him away. Parker was sitting next to their dog, covered in tissues, with an empty box nearby. "Parker!" his mum exclaimed. "What have you done?"

"Was dog," Parker shrugged.

"The dog pulled all the tissues out of the tissue box?" Parker's mum raised an eyebrow.

"Yes," Parker nodded.

Parker's mum sighed. She could tell today was the start of a very long day.

1 (a) Do you think the dog was to blame for the mess in the kitchen?

◯ Yes   ◯ No

(b) Why/why not?

_____

_____

2 Why do you think Parker blamed the dog for the mess in the kitchen?

_____

_____

CRITICAL REFLECTION

Imaginative Text

3 Circle words that describe how Parker's mum might have felt about having to clean up the mess in the kitchen.

happy	angry	annoyed
excited	tired	grateful
frustrated	joyful	surprised

4 Why do you think Parker's mum was concerned about Parker being "too quiet for far too long"? Tick the correct answer.

a) Parker might be quiet because he's up to mischief. ☐

b) She didn't know where Parker was and she was worried he was hurt. ☐

c) Parker might have fallen asleep and it wasn't time for his nap. ☐

d) Parker could have left to punish the dog for being naughty. ☐

5 (a) Do you think the dog was to blame for the mess in the bathroom?

☐ Yes   ☐ No

(b) Why/why not?

_____

_____

6 Why did Parker's mum sigh after discovering each mess? Tick the correct answer.

a) She didn't get enough sleep. ☐

b) She was frustrated by the mess. ☐

c) She didn't like cleaning. ☐

d) She was surprised by the mess. ☐

7 Parker's mum could tell it was the start of a very long day. What do you think she meant?

_____

_____

TARGETING COMPREHENSION 5 © PASCAL PRESS ISBN 9781925490640

Information Text

World events connect the world's people.

For most of human history, people across the world have not interacted due to the distances that separate them. Over time, developments in transport and communication technologies (phones, email etc.) have made distance much easier to overcome. Just 200 years ago in the British colony of New South Wales, it took eight months for information to arrive from England. Now, world events — cultural and sporting events, conflicts (war) and disasters — are reported around the world in seconds.

Events connect people because of their shared relationships. Countries respond to world disasters because they are able to help with their _____ and _____.

Did you know the number of mobile phone subscriptions is approaching the number of people on Earth?

Source: Go Facts, *World Events*, Blake Education. [abridged]

1 What is the writer saying about communication? Tick the most accurate statement.

a) There are so many mobile phones that we are 'drowning' in them. Imagine the waste! ☐

b) Communication has helped people to be more in touch and able to do something for others quickly. ☐

c) Communication used to be really slow but now it is fast. ☐

d) As we get better communication, we can help in wars more quickly. ☐

2 Why do you think 200 years ago it took so long for a message to come from England? Explain your answer.

_____

_____

_____

_____

_____

_____

CRITICAL REFLECTION

Information Text

In 1962, the United States of America and the Soviet Union were in a military stand-off (argument). This may have led to nuclear war. Communication between the countries' leaders was important but messages between them took 12 hours.

Source: Go Facts, *World Events*, Blake Education. [abridged]

3 Tick the statements that you think say how the problem of communication between America and Russia was solved. Clue: Remember, it was 1962, seven years before the first man walked on the moon.

a) The two countries installed a direct telephone line to each other which was fast and private. ☐

b) The countries decided that letters should be written and delivered by jets. ☐

c) Carrier pigeons were used to carry messages between the governments. ☐

d) Fast ships were used to carry messages. ☐

e) They began to talk by radio so that everyone could hear what was being said. ☐

4 Now that communication around the world happens in seconds instead of months, what happens when there are disasters?

_____

_____

_____

5 Proverbs are wise sayings with a message that gives good advice. 'No man is an island' is a proverb. Colour the shape that best explains this proverb in terms of communication.

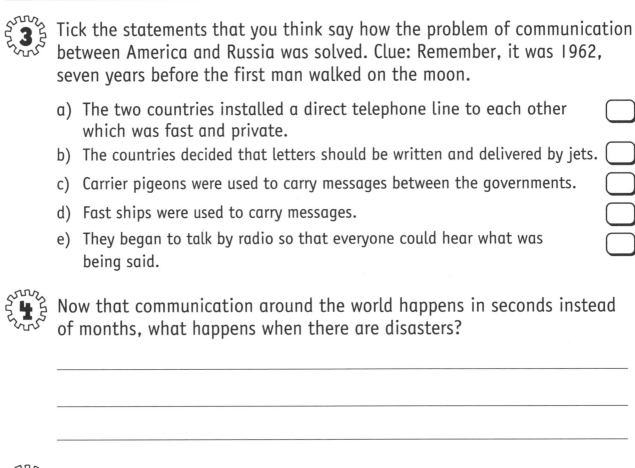

People don't do well on their own. They need to communicate their thoughts and feelings to others.

Communication between islands is very important.

People can't live alone because we need communication.

We need to live on islands a lot more. They are great for communication.

TARGETING COMPREHENSION 5 © PASCAL PRESS ISBN 9781925490640

CRITICAL REFLECTION

Pollution has many faces — none of them pretty. Our world is suffering because we have allowed our air, water and soil to become polluted. We must take action NOW to preserve these most precious resources.

Aerosols (liquid and solid particles) contaminate the air. They come from car and truck exhaust, factories, dust and pollen, bushfires and volcanoes. Many aerosols enter the air when we burn fossil fuels such as coal and petrol. We must stop this dangerous practice. With every breath of polluted air we take, we risk developing serious health problems. We must work toward alternative energy sources such as hydro, solar and wind power, and the production of **bio-fuels** (fuel made from trees, sugar cane, grasses and crop waste).

We have contaminated our soil with **toxins** (poisons) by the careless dumping of industrial and household waste, and the overuse of fertilisers and pesticides. These toxins enter the food chain through the crops we grow and can be harmful to our health. We must urgently adopt the practice of 'Reduce Reuse Recycle' — we could, for example, reduce our waste by shopping more wisely; use alternatives to throwaway products such as straws and disposable cups and recycle glass bottles and cans.

Toxins also contaminate our waterways. They enter our rivers and oceans through household sewage, agricultural waste and industrial wastewater. Polluted water is a serious threat to our health, yet we continue to dump harmful chemicals, oils, detergents and contaminated liquids down the sink. They DO NOT just disappear — they end up in our sewage systems.

An added problem is the careless dumping of rubbish, especially plastics, which ends up in our waterways and oceans, endangering our marine life.

We have created our pollution problems largely by dumping our waste into the air, water and soil. We must all take steps to dispose of our waste thoughtfully, so we can all enjoy the gift of clean air, sweet water and fertile soil.

CRITICAL REFLECTION

 1 What is the main idea of this text? Tick the best answer.

a) Pollution is a serious threat to our health.

b) Plastics endanger our marine life.

c) Air, soil and water pollution is caused by the careless disposal of waste.

d) Waste products disappear when you dump them.

Persuasive Text

2 The writer suggests that we 'Reduce Reuse Recycle' to limit waste. List three things you could do to have less waste in your home.

_____

_____

_____

3 What is the effect of plastic waste in our oceans? Tick any that apply.

a) Sea creatures can become entangled in plastic and drown or starve because they are unable to find food. ☐

b) Plastic waste sinks to the bottom of the sea and has no effect on marine life. ☐

c) Sea creatures cannot digest plastic if they eat it, so they can die of suffocation or starvation. ☐

d) It's fun for fish, seabirds and turtles to play with coloured plastic objects. ☐

4 Why do you think the government has banned single-use plastic bags?

a) to encourage people to buy less ☐

b) to reduce plastic waste in landfill and oceans ☐

c) to close down the plastics industry ☐

d) to allow supermarkets to make more money by selling plastic bags ☐

5 Glass, paper and mesh bags are good alternatives to plastic packaging. Name four supermarket items currently packaged in plastic, which could be sold in glass containers or paper bags.

_____   _____

_____   _____

6 Select the best title for this text.

a) Pollution has many faces ☐

b) Reduce! Reuse! Recycle! ☐

c) What a Waste! ☐

d) Protect our World from Pollution ☐

TARGETING COMPREHENSION 5 © PASCAL PRESS ISBN 9781925490640

Quick Guide to:

• SYNTHESIS •

Many creatures and plants in nature have in-built calendars. Unfortunately, these can often only be used at the cost of the organism's life.

Take the mighty whale, for example. Researchers who find the carcasses (bodies) of dead whales washed up on beaches, usually try to discover what killed them. Part of this process involves finding out how old a whale is. Death through old age needs to be ruled out. Within a whale's ear there is a small bone. Like the growth rings in a tree, this bone has rings, each of which indicates (shows) a year of life. As mentioned, most woody plants have growth rings that show a year of the plant's life.

There is, however, one animal which may remain alive when it is studied. This sea creature lays down a _____ of hard _____ yearly. Most people see this when it is dead and faded, washed up on the shore. People collect these sea creatures not knowing how old they may be. Remarkably when alive, they may be stunningly colourful ...

Answering questions about text often means finding the answer in what you have read. Sometimes you are asked to remember what was in the text. These are **literal** questions.

> **Example of a literal question:**
> What are two things that have growth rings showing their age?
>
> **Answer:** Whales and trees both have growth rings.

Synthesis is the merging (putting together) of new information with existing knowledge. When we can bring all the information together and understand it, we are able to create new and different ideas.

> **Example of a synthesis question:** The writer tells of another creature commonly found on the shore. What do you think it is and how would you tell its age?
>
> **Answer:** The creature may be a seashell. Many seashells have layers that are easily seen whether the shell is dead or alive.

DID YOU NOTICE?

To answer this question, the reader needed to have some knowledge about the seashore and what is found and collected by people as they walk along the beach.

SYNTHESIS

Rain pelted against the window and Jo huddled under the covers. The storm was definitely closing in. Crack! Boom! The lightning flashed behind the curtains and lit up the dark room.

A shadowy figure appeared at the doorway and knocked softly. "Jo, are you awake?"

"Yes," came the timid reply.

Jo's older brother Evan walked into the room. "Just thought I'd come in to … uh … see how good the lightning looks from your room."

"Ok." Jo's voice was muffled by the covers drawn up under her nose.

Evan sat on the edge of the bed. "It's pretty loud, huh?"

Crack! Boom!

Before Jo could even reply, another roll of thunder erupted directly above the house. Jo winced and pulled the covers a little higher.

"I bet Mum and Dad have a great view from the restaurant," Evan said, trying to distract Jo from the storm.

Jo nodded quickly, with only eyes and hair visible above the tightly clenched sheets.

"Want me to put your bedside light on?" Evan asked. Jo nodded. "I … I could stay here for a while longer if you wanted me to. You know, to … uh … get a better view of the storm." Jo nodded again.

1 Why do you think Jo huddled under the covers? Tick the correct answer.

a) Jo is scared of everything. ☐

b) Jo was worried because their parents weren't home. ☐

c) Jo is scared of thunderstorms. ☐

d) Jo was cold because it was winter. ☐

2 How does this text relate to your own experience of a storm?

_____

_____

3 Explain how this text is similar to another text you've read or a movie you've seen.

_____

_____

4 Draw a picture in the box below that illustrates a scene from the text. Write a short sentence to explain what is happening in the picture.

_____

_____

5 What message/s do you think the author is trying to convey in this text? Tick any that apply.

a) It's OK to be scared sometimes. ☐

b) We should be kind to people who are scared. ☐

c) Thunderstorms are very dangerous. ☐

d) Parents should never leave their kids alone. ☐

6 Why do you think Evan said he could stay in Jo's room to get a better view of the storm?

_____

_____

Information Text

Since 1947, Australia has sent more than 30 000 men and women to join 62 United Nations peacekeeping operations.

The United Nations has its own security force, drawn from member countries. Its role is to help countries torn by conflict create conditions for peace. Peacekeepers do not use force except in self-defence.

Australians were the first United Nations peacekeepers ever to go into the field, in Indonesia in 1947.

United Nations workers wear "United Nations blue". The organisation chose blue because it is the opposite of red, the colour of war.

Source: Go Facts, *Australia at War*, Blake Education. [abridged]

1 Because the UN military forces are made up of people from many countries, there are a number of difficulties to overcome. Select the statement that best says what these may be.

United Nations soldiers may have difficulties because ...

a) many languages are spoken, and the cultures, religions and food are all different. ☐

b) some countries don't like the colour blue and make their soldiers wear green instead. ☐

c) people who make decisions all talk different languages and it is hard to give orders. ☐

d) they are a long way from home and become homesick. ☐

2 Women are an important part of the United Nations peacekeeping forces. Although they don't fight, what do you think their role (job) is? Clue: Think about the women and children who need help in countries where there is war.

_____

_____

_____

_____

SYNTHESIS

TARGETING COMPREHENSION 5 © PASCAL PRESS ISBN 9781925490640

Australians have commanded six United Nations peacekeeping operations. Major General Peter Cosgrove commanded Interfet (a UN peacekeeping operation). He became Australia's governor-general in 2014.

Source: Go Facts, *Australia at War*, Blake Education. [abridged]

 3 Colours are symbols for things in the world. For example, flags have national colours on them. Read the statements below and try to match them with the colours by drawing a line.

Meaning		Colour
The colour of peace.		pink
The colour of nature.		black
The colour of love and romance.		green
The colour of evil.		white

 4 Choose **two** of the colours you matched above and explain why you made matches with meanings. Give reasons and examples of why you made your choices.

_____

_____

_____

_____

Australians have fought in wars all over the world in the last 100 years. Many of our men and women have given their lives so that we may remain free. We have a proud tradition of helping countries fight dangers and evil.

Soldiers killed in far-off lands are remembered with tombstones but some are lost forever. Some of our friends and former enemies say that our soldiers have become their sons and now rest in their soil.

 5 What do you think other countries feel about Australia's contribution to wars and the United Nations?

_____

_____

_____

SYNTHESIS

Text 1. Never skin (free) dive by yourself. Getting into the water without a buddy watching your back is inviting an accident.

Drowning is just one of the hazards — sharks are another. Australia's waters have some of the deadliest creatures on the planet. Risking being bitten, stung or eaten are the dangers faced by swimmers and divers alike. Even those colourful, pretty little shells you may collect can kill!

Diving by yourself isn't worth your life! Never dive alone!

Text 2. Dropping silently from the reef into the clear, salty water, my eyes adjusted to the light. Seeing a beautifully planned garden, my senses were filled with vivid colours and strange shapes. John, my brother, was on the way. I'd just been quicker to get dressed, eat my breakfast and get to the reef.

I sensed him behind and swirled around in a blur of bubbles. Facing me was a _____. The pit of my stomach collapsed.

1 Where would you have read the first text? Tick the box that best says this.

The first text may have been printed in ...

a) a magazine saying that Australian beaches are safe and there is no danger.

b) a television advertisement about 'fun in the sun' in Australia.

c) a book about deadly creatures.

d) an advertisement for an underwater adventure company.

2 Tourist businesses may not find text one helpful. What may tourists think if they visit Australia?

_____

_____

_____

_____

_____

TARGETING COMPREHENSION 5 © PASCAL PRESS ISBN 9781925490640

Persuasive Text

3 What advice would you give to the person in text 2? Include what may happen in your answer.

_____

_____

_____

_____

4 Write a newspaper headline for text 2.

> Having a poisonous barb on the end of its proboscis (like an arm) which has a neuro-toxin (a poison that affects nerves, muscles, movement etc.), cone shells may be deadly to divers if touched. Their poison may paralyse the muscles in the chest, preventing breathing.

5 Read the text above about cone shells. Why are cone shells deadly to people who skin or free dive?

_____

_____

_____

6 A proverb is an old saying which gives advice or tells us important information. Circle the proverb that suits the text about cone shells. Write why you think so in the box.

_____	a) Better late than never.
_____	b) There's no place like home.
_____	c) Good things come to those who wait.
_____	d) Only fools jump in.

Literal

Animals have certain features and adaptations that help them to survive in the environment in which they live. These adaptations, or changes, happen over a long period of time.

Adaptations can be physical features, known as 'structural' adaptations. Things animals actually do in order to survive are known as 'behavioural' adaptations.

The camel has a number of structural adaptations that help it survive the dry, hot conditions in the desert. These include two rows of long, thick eyelashes that keep the sand out of their eyes, and nostrils they can close so they don't breathe in the sand when it's windy. Camels also have wide hooves to stop them sinking into the sand while walking.

Did you know?

A camel's hump is actually made out of fat. This structural adaptation helps it survive for a long time without food and water.

One very important behavioural adaptation is that camels can drink over 100 litres of water at a time. This enables them to survive in the desert for many days.

Animal adaptations are important if animals are to survive in a changing environment.

 1 True or False? Animal adaptations develop over a long period of time.

◯ True   ◯ False

 2 Draw a line to join the term with the correct definition.

Term	Definition
Physical adaptations	Actions that help animals survive
Behavioural adaptations	Bodily features that help animals survive

3 Which adaptation helps keep sand out of camels' eyes? Tick the correct answer.

a) wide hooves   ◯

b) nostrils that close   ◯

c) their hump   ◯

d) thick eyelashes   ◯

TARGETING COMPREHENSION 5 © PASCAL PRESS ISBN 9781925490640

Literal

4 True or False? Camels' humps are filled with water.

◯ True   ◯ False

5 Fill in the missing words.

Being able to drink large amounts of water at once is an example of a

_____ adaptation.

6 Label the picture of the camel below to show four physical adaptations.

7 Why is the ability to drink large amounts of water at once an important adaptation for camels?

_____

_____

8 Explain why animal adaptations are important.

_____

_____

TARGETING COMPREHENSION 5 © PASCAL PRESS ISBN 9781925490640

ASSESSMENT

Inferring

Clank! Clank! Clank!

The sound of metal against metal echoed in the dimly lit workshop.

Clank! Clank! Clonk!

"Aargh!" An anguished cry rang out across the room.

Phillipa shook her hand and rubbed it, then peered carefully at the blueprints on the desk in front of her. The world's first personal holographic device. It was going to be her finest triumph. Well … her only triumph … but a triumph nonetheless.

Phillipa's eyes glazed over as she dreamily imagined the many uses for her latest invention. Placing it in her bedroom so it looked like she was in bed while she was really staying up late inventing. Putting it on her seat in the classroom so it looked like she was attending her English class — the possibilities were endless.

Picking up the soldering iron, Phillipa squinted at the wires she needed to connect. It was time to test the unit's electrical circuit. Flicking a switch on the side of the device, Phillipa started to hear a whirring sound. Her eyes grew wide as the device began to light up.

The whirring got louder and louder. The device started shaking. Suddenly, it released a small puff of smoke and everything came to a stop. Frowning, Phillipa examined her diagram of the electrical circuit. "Ah …" she mused, "I think I've got it!"

 1 (a) On a scale of 1 to 5, how well do you think Phillipa can use her invention tools? Circle a number.

1   2   3   4   5

(b) Give a reason for your rating above.

_____

_____

 2 Using information from the text, what do you think 'anguished' means? Tick the correct answer.

a) happy

b) sad

c) painful

d) angry

TARGETING COMPREHENSION 5 © PASCAL PRESS ISBN 9781925490640

ASSESSMENT

Inferring

3 (a) Do you think Phillipa's new invention will be a success?

☐ Yes   ☐ No

(b) What makes you say that?

_____

_____

4 Tick the correct answer.
Given a choice, Phillipa would prefer to ...

a) go to bed on time.   ☐

b) create new inventions.   ☐

c) attend her English class.   ☐

5 True or False? A soldering iron is used to join metal together.

☐ True   ☐ False

6 How did Phillipa feel when the text said: "Her eyes grew wide as the device began to light up"? Tick the correct answer.

a) scared   ☐

b) angry   ☐

c) happy   ☐

d) excited   ☐

7 Why do you think the device started to shake and release a puff of smoke?

_____

_____

8 On the scale below, show how likely it is that Phillipa will give up trying to create her invention. Circle your answer.

Very likely   Likely   Unlikely   Very unlikely

Predicting

Clunk! Jo closed the visor on her helmet and gripped the wheel tightly.
"All good?" her uncle asked from the sideline. Jo gave a determined thumbs up.

1 What type of text do you think this will be? Tick the correct answer.

a) persuasive ☐

b) imaginative ☐

c) informative ☐

Foot set against the accelerator, Jo waited for the lights at the side of the track to change. She ignored the other racers on either side and stared at the road ahead.
"Ready! Set! Go!"

2 On the scale below, show how quickly you think Jo will take off at the start of the race. Circle the correct answer.

Very slowly   Slowly   Quickly   Very quickly

Tires screeching, Jo stomped down hard on the accelerator as her go-kart sped to the front of the pack. Her uncle jumped up and down on the sidelines, watching her blistering start.

3 Using the information in the text so far, how likely is it that Jo will win the race? Circle your answer.

Very unlikely   Unlikely   Likely   Very likely

The other racers stared at Jo's go-kart as it sped ahead. Coming up to the first turn, Jo looked through the corner and accelerated out of the turn. The other racers were hot on her tail — there was no room for error.

One particular driver crept closer than the rest. Jo could hear someone was close, but she stared at the track with a determined gaze. They both drove aggressively around one corner and then the next, their tyres squealing. With every corner, the other driver's go-kart drew closer and closer to the barrier next to the road.

4 (a) Do you think the other driver will beat Jo?

☐ Yes   ☐ No

(b) What makes you say that?

_____

TARGETING COMPREHENSION 5 © PASCAL PRESS ISBN 9781925490640

The next corner was a tight hairpin turn — Jo backed off the accelerator and spun the wheel. The driver behind her pushed on at speed and crashed into the barriers next to the track. Jo heard the collision but didn't look back. The driver would be okay. She needed to concentrate.

5 What is most likely to happen next? Tick your answer.

a) Jo worries about the other driver and loses concentration. ⬜

b) Jo drives too fast around the next corner and crashes. ⬜

c) Jo focuses on the race and winning. ⬜

Left-hand turn. Right-hand turn. As Jo sped closer to the finish line, she could practically see the black and white chequered flag at the end. Staying focused as she rounded the last bend, Jo approached the final straight. As she rammed the accelerator to the floor, pushing the go-kart as fast as it could go, Jo suddenly felt a jolt from behind. Someone had caught up to her and had rammed her go-kart! Furious, Jo gripped the wheel to keep her go-kart on the track.

6 What is most likely to happen next? Tick your answer.

a) Jo will lose control of her go-kart. ⬜

b) The other driver will crash. ⬜

c) Jo will win the race. ⬜

d) The other driver will win. ⬜

Hurtling ever closer to the finish line, Jo could see the driver who had rammed her go-kart out of the corner of her eye. They were closing in fast! Jo leant forward with intent, urging her go-kart to go just that little bit faster. Closer … closer … and zoom! The go-karts whizzed across the finish line.

Jo stepped out of her go-kart triumphantly and took off her helmet. "Well done," said the driver who had crashed earlier.

"Good race!" exclaimed another.

"Sorry, love," a voice piped up. "I didn't mean to bump your go-kart."

"That's OK, Mum!" laughed Jo. "Racing with my family made this the best birthday ever!"

7 True or False? Jo will be mad later that her mum bumped the go-kart.

⬜ True   ⬜ False

ASSESSMENT

Analysing

Guide dogs help people who are visually impaired or blind, to move safely and be more independent. They help their owners to navigate their way through different places like parks, streets and shops.

In order for a puppy to become a guide dog, it must develop the ability to concentrate, show good initiative, be keen to work and show self-control around other animals.

Guide dog puppies go through a special two-year training program. Volunteer puppy trainers raise the dogs and teach them simple commands like 'sit', 'stay' and 'drop'. During this time, the puppies also get used to other dogs. When the puppies are a year-and-a-half old, they have six months of special training to learn how to manage distractions in loud and crowded places. They also learn a variety of special skills.

Guide dogs are taught to obey instructions from their owners: find paths, doors and steps; lead their owners to destinations, such as their school or where they work; and help their owners avoid obstacles, such as bicycles, people or overhead branches. The dogs also learn how to lie down quietly for a period of time in restaurants or work situations. Interestingly, guide dogs are also taught to refuse commands from their owners that might lead the owner into danger.

If you see a guide dog wearing a harness, it means the guide dog is 'working' and you shouldn't pat or distract the dog. However, owners will take the guide dog's harness off sometimes, so they can play and relax.

Guide dogs help their owners in so many ways. By giving people who are blind or visually impaired the support to be more confident and independent, they are helping people to live happier and safer lives.

1 What is this text about? Tick any that apply.

a) how guide dogs are trained ☐

b) why guide dogs are the best dogs ☐

c) who can train guide dogs ☐

d) special skills guide dogs learn ☐

2 What is the purpose of this text? Tick the correct answer.

a) to inform ☐

b) to entertain ☐

c) to persuade ☐

TARGETING COMPREHENSION 5 © PASCAL PRESS ISBN 9781925490640

Analysing

3 Why do guide dogs need to be trained?

_____

_____

4 Why are guide dogs important?

_____

_____

5 What could happen if you pat or distract a dog while it is wearing a harness?

_____

_____

6 Why would it be important for owners to sometimes take the guide dog's harness off? Tick the correct answer.

a) The harness might get itchy. ☐

b) Dogs need time to rest and play. ☐

c) They need to wash the dog's harness. ☐

d) Other people can play with their dog. ☐

ASSESSMENT

We Need More Time to Play, OK?

It's vital that kids have more time to play. Kids have long school days filled with lessons, and often have activities before and after school as well. Without more playtime, how will we ever become as creative, imaginative and healthy as we can be?

Let's face the facts. Kids go to school five days a week and most of this time is spent sitting down at our desks. Apart from sport or physical education lessons, we don't get much of a chance to move around. We only get a quick break in the morning and our lunchtimes feel short as well. If we don't have enough long breaks to run around and play, as well as eat our food, how will be ever become healthy and strong?

Some kids get the chance to exercise before or after school — they might have swimming lessons or soccer practice. But this isn't really play. People are telling you what to do and when, and you don't get the chance to use your imagination. Many kids are missing out on the benefits of play even on the weekend because they have so many planned activities.

Kids must be given free time in which to be creative. We need to invent games, design new rules, build cubbyhouses and develop new friendships. Instead of scheduling soccer drills, could we just invite a friend to play in the backyard? Instead of swimming laps every morning, could we just go to the local pool with our mates on the weekend? Instead of sitting at our desks, could we have an extra break in the afternoon at school?

By giving kids the time to play, you're not only helping them to develop healthy and active minds and bodies, you're helping them to just be kids. Kids need to be given more time to play.

1 (a) Do you believe that you have enough playtime?

◯ Yes   ◯ No

(b) Give a reason/s for your answer.

_____

_____

Making Connections

2 Why does the writer think more playtime is needed?

_____

_____

3 If I felt like the kid who wrote this text, I would ...

_____

_____

4 What were your feelings when you read this? Why did you feel this way?

I felt _____ because _____

5 How is this text similar to something else you've read or seen?

Think about: the topic, the information and vocabulary in the text, what you've seen on TV, things you have studied, or conversations you've had.

_____

_____

_____

6 Imagine you are the author of this text. Create your own solution or idea that would work at your school or in your life.

_____

_____

_____

Dogs are the Best Friends

Why are dogs the best friends ever? Dogs are good friends because they are loyal, kind and funny. They also love to play and want to spend time with you — in fact, I believe dogs are better friends than people.

Good friends are loyal companions. People sometimes forget about their friends when they meet new people, making their old friends lonely. However, dogs are always faithful to you — they might make new friends too, but you will always be the most special person in the world according to your dog.

People who are good friends are kind to each other. Sometimes human friends are mean to each other on purpose. However, dogs are always kind. Seeing Eye dogs learn to help people who are blind or visually impaired; and sniffer dogs learn to help their owners find dangerous things in order to keep everyone safe. Dogs are never mean to their owners.

Best friends want to hang out together a lot. Sometimes people don't want to play with you, or they decide to play with someone else. However, dogs never get bored of playing games with you, and they love spending time with you — even if you're just sitting together.

Sometimes people let you down, but dogs will always stay by your side. There are so many reasons why everyone calls them man's best friend.

 1 What is the viewpoint supported in this text?

_____

_____

 2 Why did the author compose this text? Tick the correct answer.

a) to tell a funny story about dogs and friends ☐

b) to tell readers that dogs make great friends ☐

c) to give people information about dogs ☐

d) to list instructions on how to make friends ☐

Critical Reflection

3 What is the author's purpose? Tick the correct answer.

a) to convince the reader ☐

b) to entertain the reader ☐

c) to inform the reader ☐

4 What could be another suitable title for this text? Tick the best answer.

a) People are Bad Friends ☐

b) Why My Best Friend is a Dog ☐

c) Dogs vs. People ☐

d) Friends are Important ☐

5 Using the information from this text, how true is it that dogs are really man's best friend? Circle the correct answer.

Very untrue   Untrue   True   Very true

6 If this was a debate, what could someone say as an effective argument for why people are better friends than dogs?

_____

_____

_____

ASSESSMENT

Our Place in Space

There are countless planets throughout the known universe. Scientists are always discovering more of them. Although our planet is one of many, it really is quite unique.

In order to survive, we need the temperature to be just right. Although it can get hot in places like Australia, some of the planets would be much too hot for us to even survive, and other planets are far too cold.

Planet	Mercury	Venus	Earth	Mars	Jupiter	Saturn	Uranus	Neptune
Average Temperature	167 °C	464 °C	15 °C	–65 °C	–110 °C	–140 °C	–195 °C	–200 °C

Water is vital in order for us to live. Scientists think that Mars, our moon and some of Jupiter's moons might have some frozen water on them. However, Earth is the only planet known to have lasting bodies of liquid water.

Although scientists haven't found any other planets with food or plants like we have here on Earth, that doesn't mean they have stopped searching for them. Some scientists spend their whole lives studying the universe, hoping to discover something new.

Considering our planet Earth is just the right temperature and has the water, plants and food we need in order to live, it looks like we have a pretty special place in space.

 1 (a) Name something you already knew about space before you read this text.

_____

_____

(b) Explain how this fact is related to the information in the text.

_____

_____

TARGETING COMPREHENSION 5 © PASCAL PRESS ISBN 9781925490640

Synthesis

 2 Explain why Earth is a unique planet.

_____

_____

 3 What is the most important message the author is trying to tell us? Tick the correct answer.

a) There are lots of planets in the universe. ☐

b) Some planets are very hot while others are very cold. ☐

c) Earth is the only known planet where we could survive. ☐

d) It's hard to find liquid water on other planets. ☐

 4 Write two questions you would ask the author to find out more about this topic.

a) _____

b) _____

 5 Create your own suitable title for this text.

_____

_____